D1113194

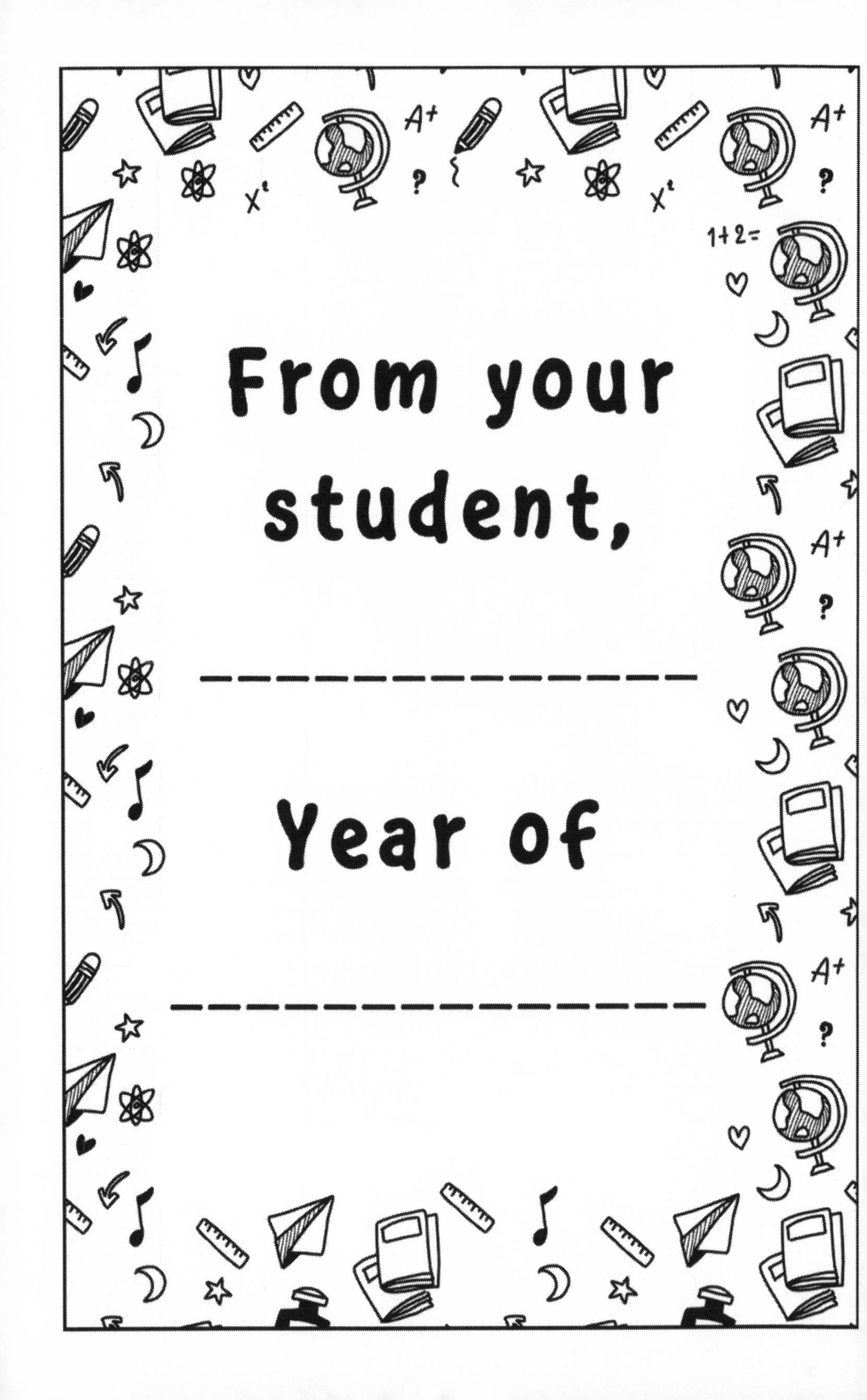
From your student,
____
Year of
____

A+
1+2=

You are
really
great at

This year
you taught
me about

A+
x²
?
1+2=
You made me
feel special
when

A+
1+2=

I loved it when our class

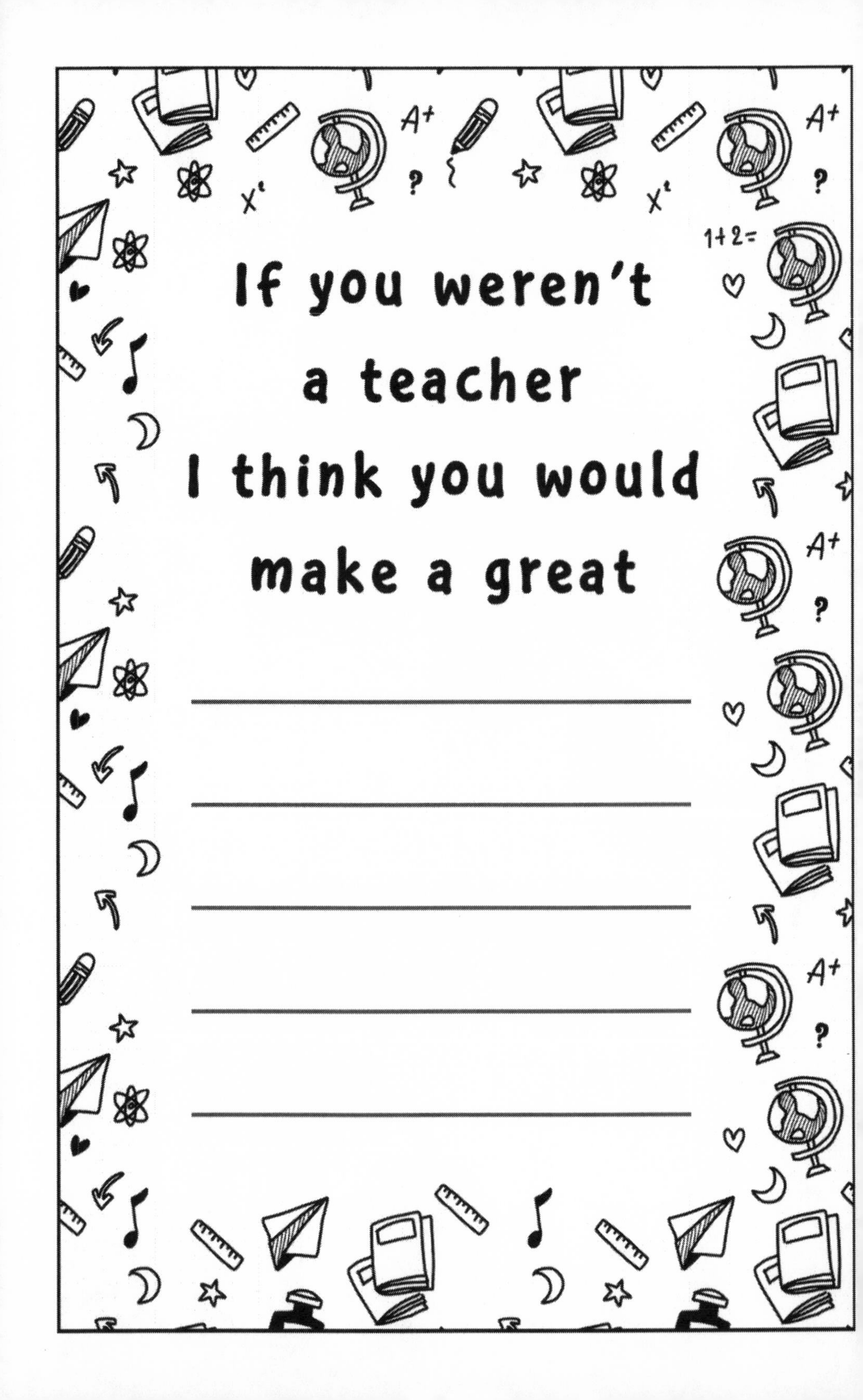

If you weren't a teacher I think you would make a great

A+
1+2=

You are super awesome teacher because

____

____

____

____

____

When You Teach, It Feels Like

You are
than you think

Having
spent time
with you, I

Before
I met you,
I was

When

I see you

____

It makes me

____

____

____

____

My
favorite joke
you tell class is

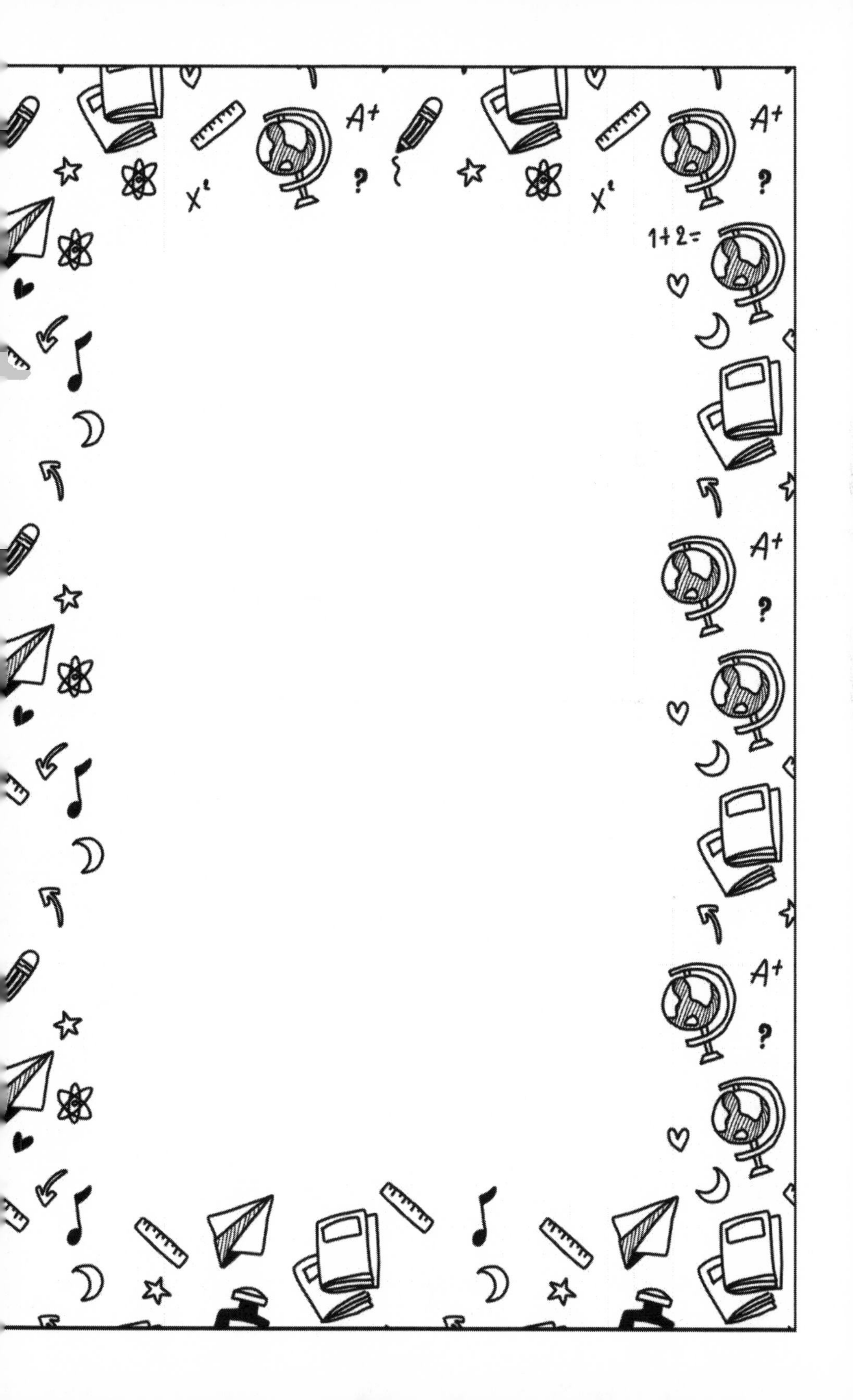

Your
special talent
is definitely

Here is a map
of our classroom
(in case you get lost!)

I really liked our
because

My favorite
thing on you desk is
Here is a
picture of it

I think you will be

because

If I were

I would definetly

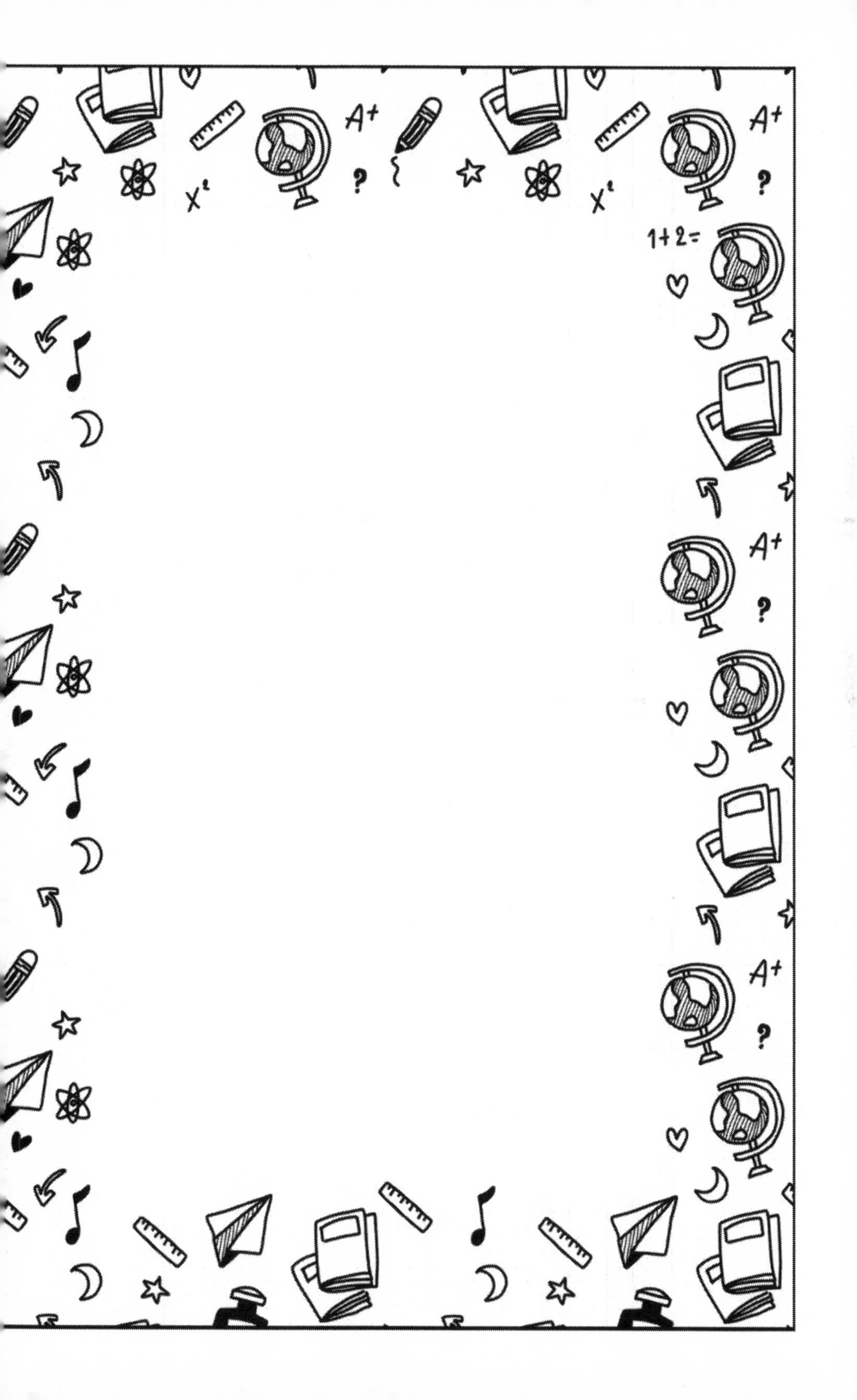

I want you to know that you are

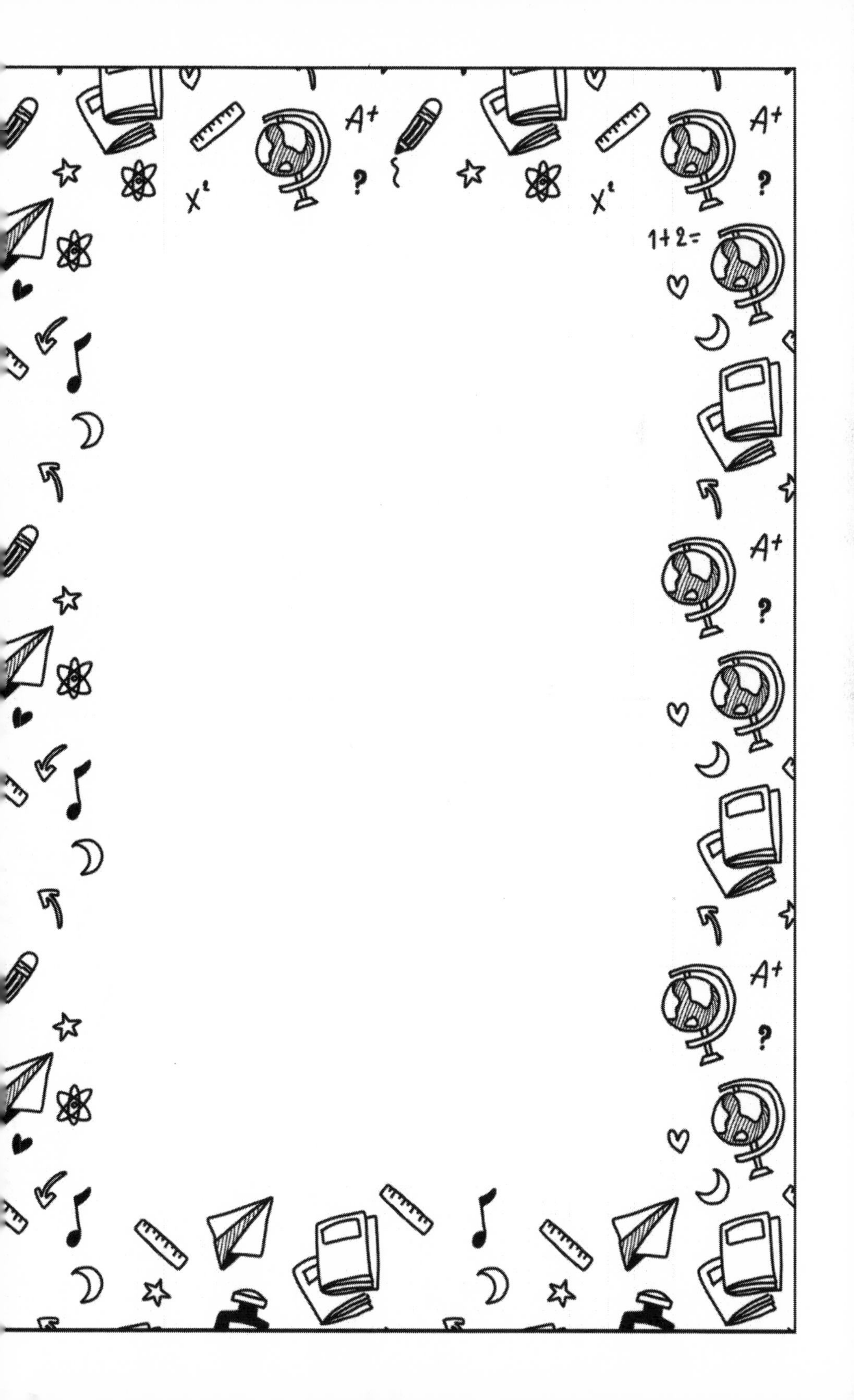
A+
1+2=

I
love how you

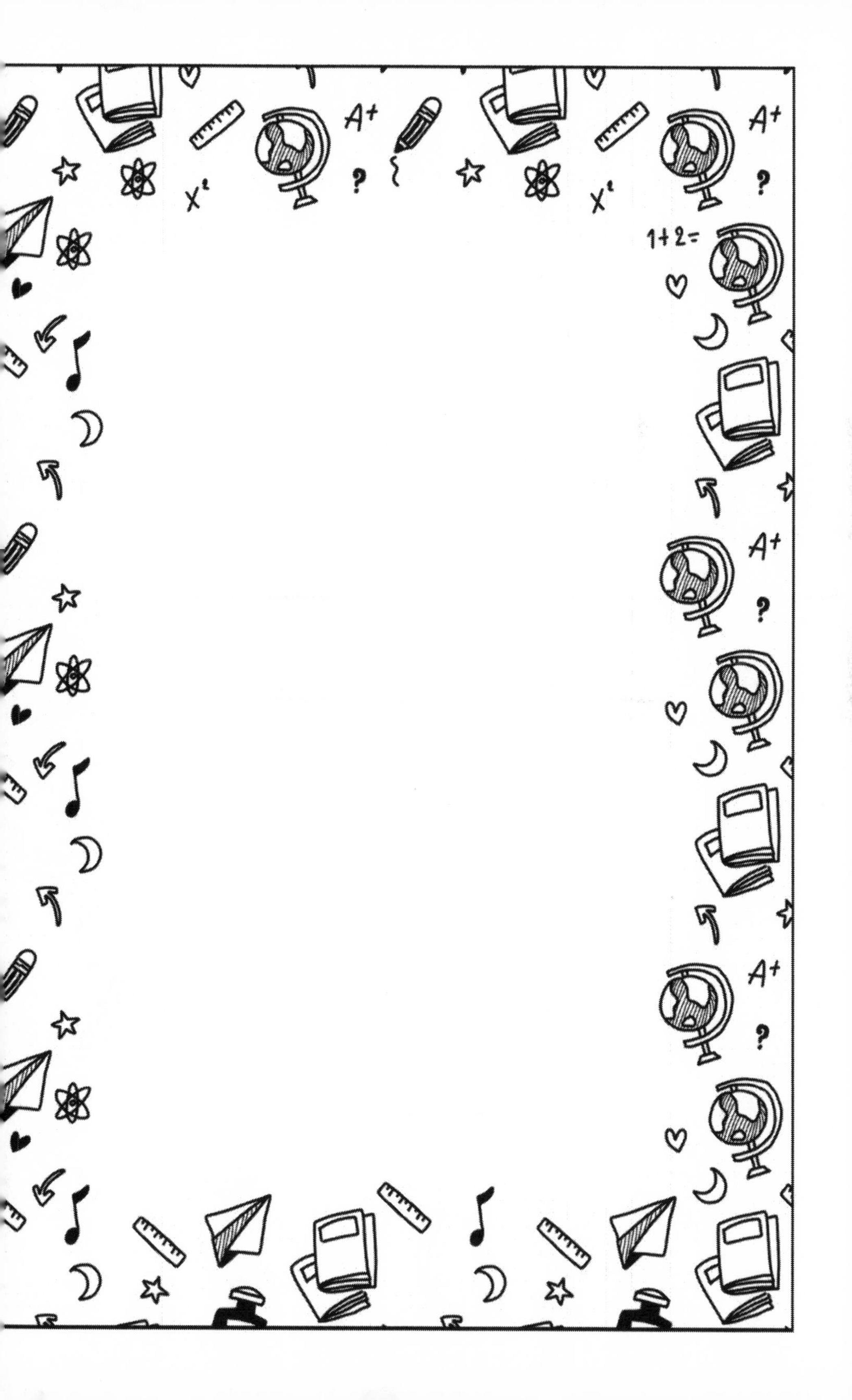

You always
help me to
A+
?
x^2
1+2=

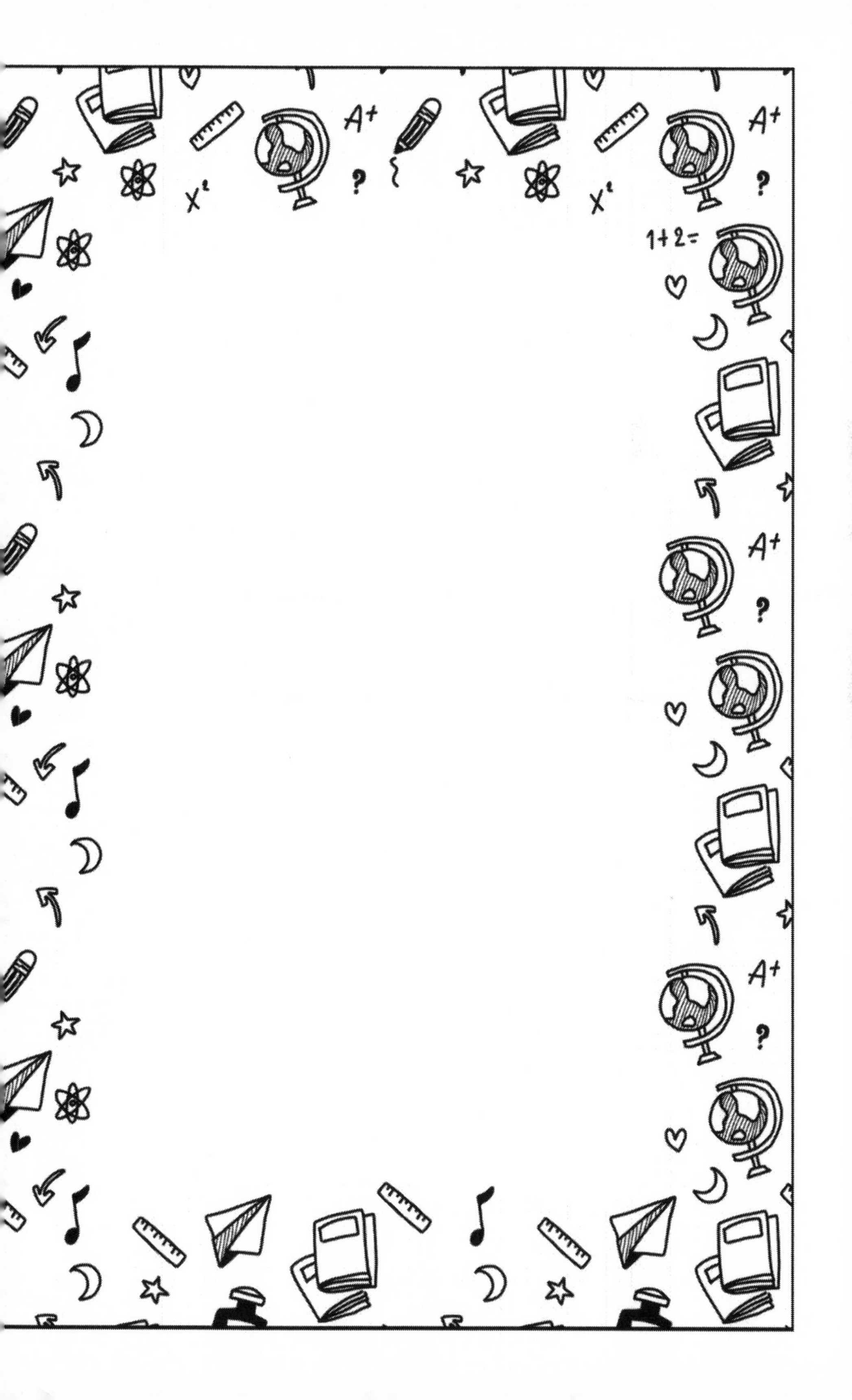

I like when
you call me

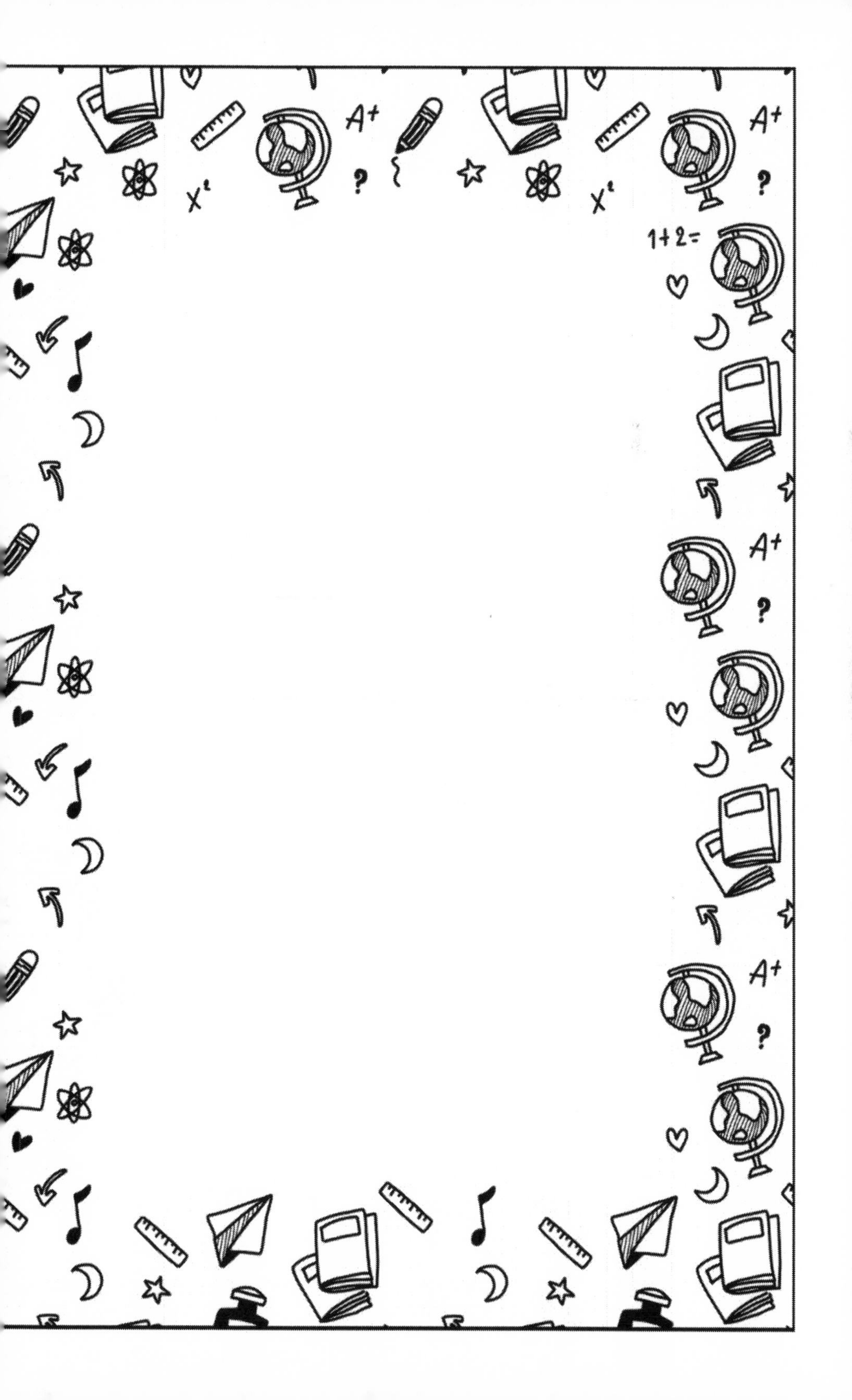

You are
smarter than

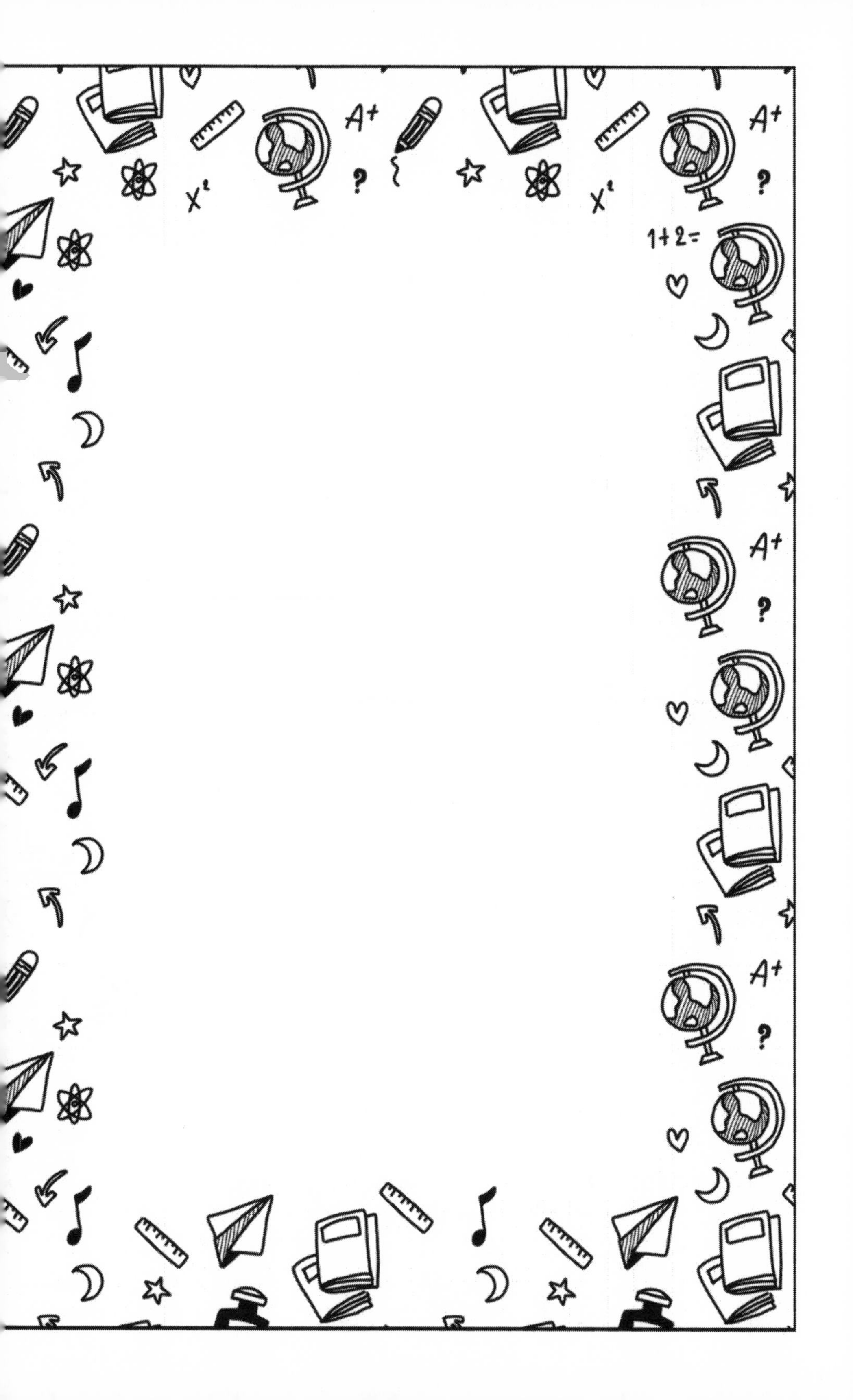

You work
hard at
A+
1+2=

If I had
million bucks
I would buy you
A+
?
1+2=

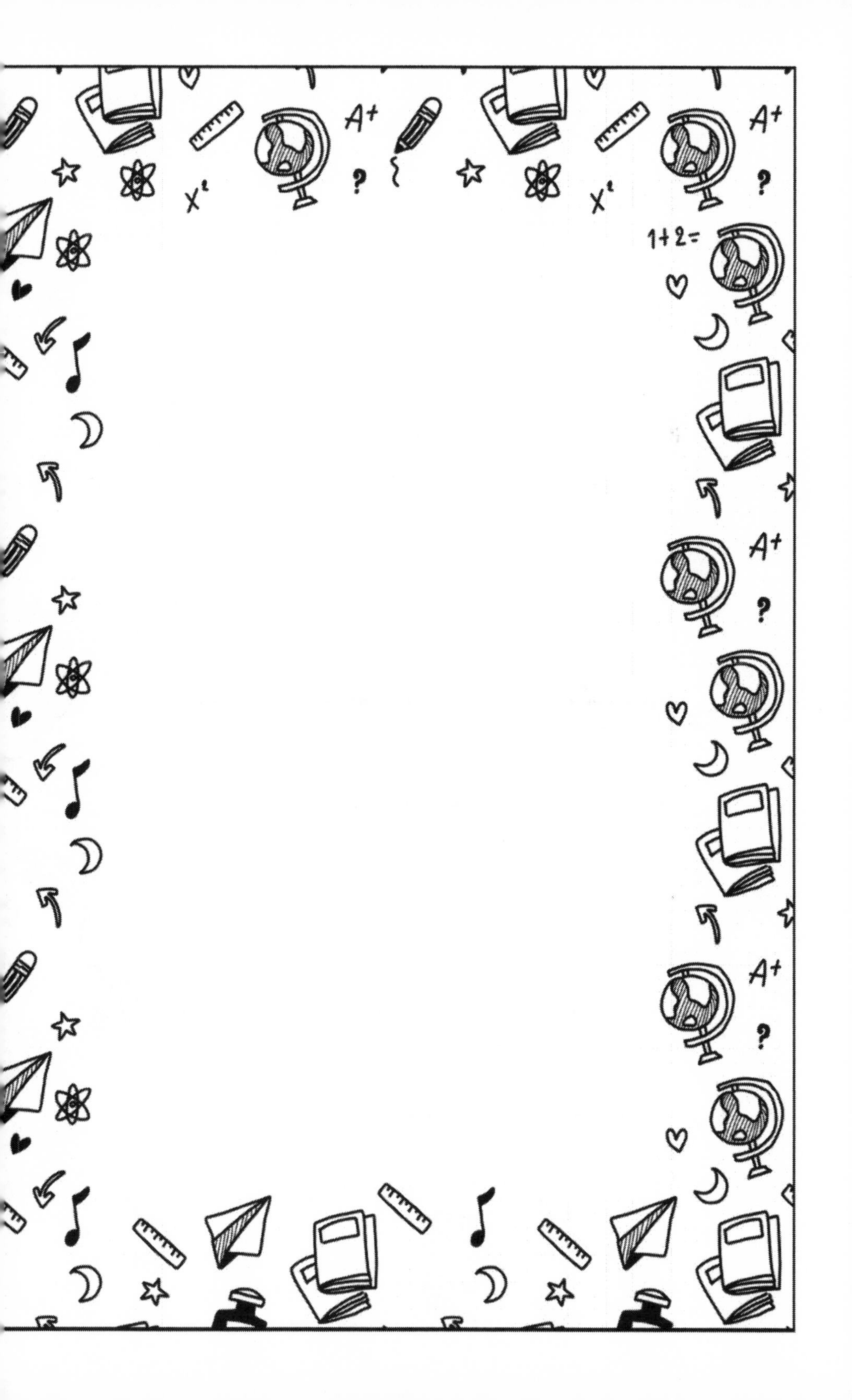

Best thing
about your job
is

Our favorite
thing to do
together is

what I am going to miss most is
A+
?
x²
1+2=

A+
X²
?
1+2=

My favorite
memory
about you is

I would
buy you
a million
A+
A+
A+
A+
1+2=

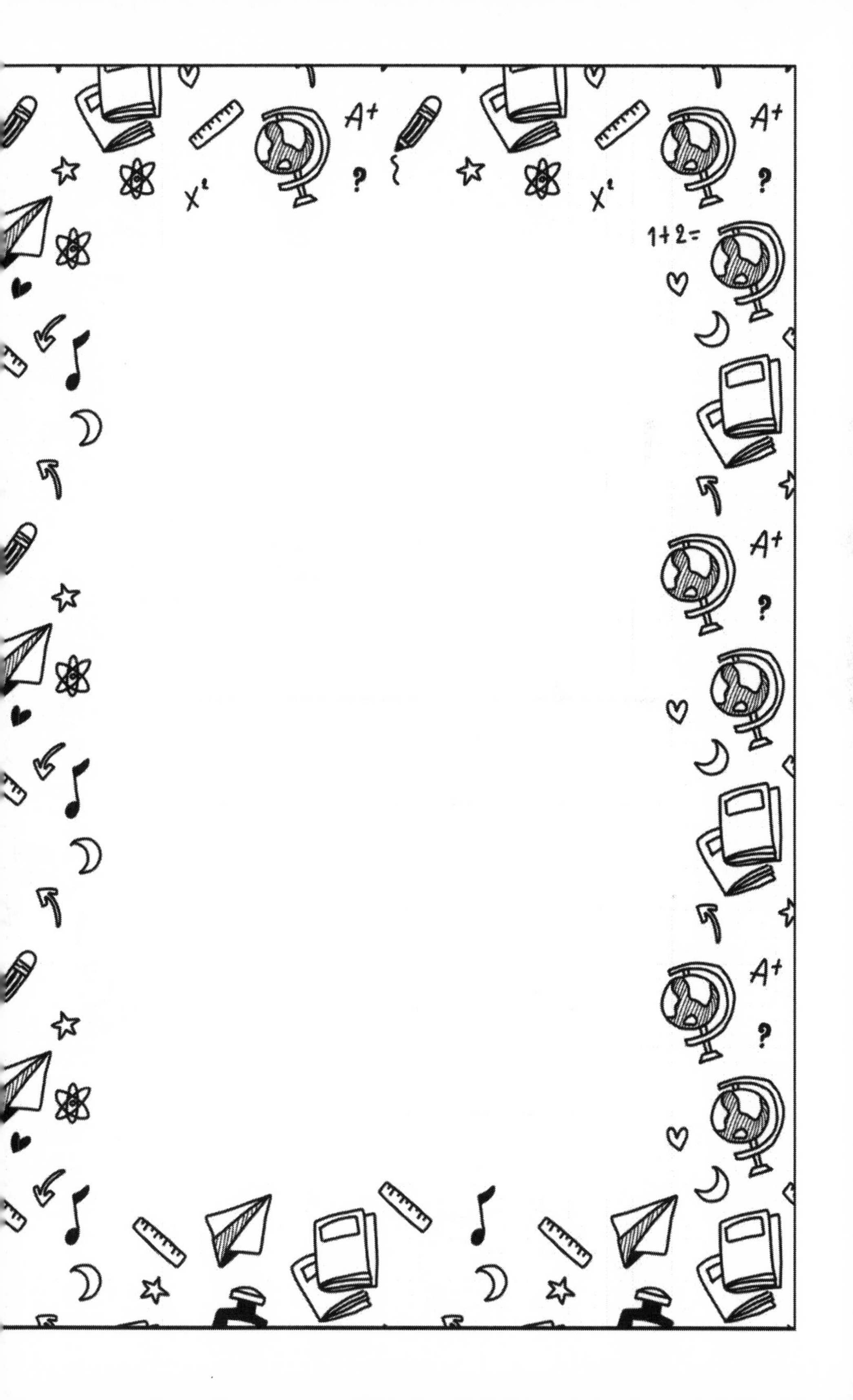
A+
1+2=

I wish
I had your

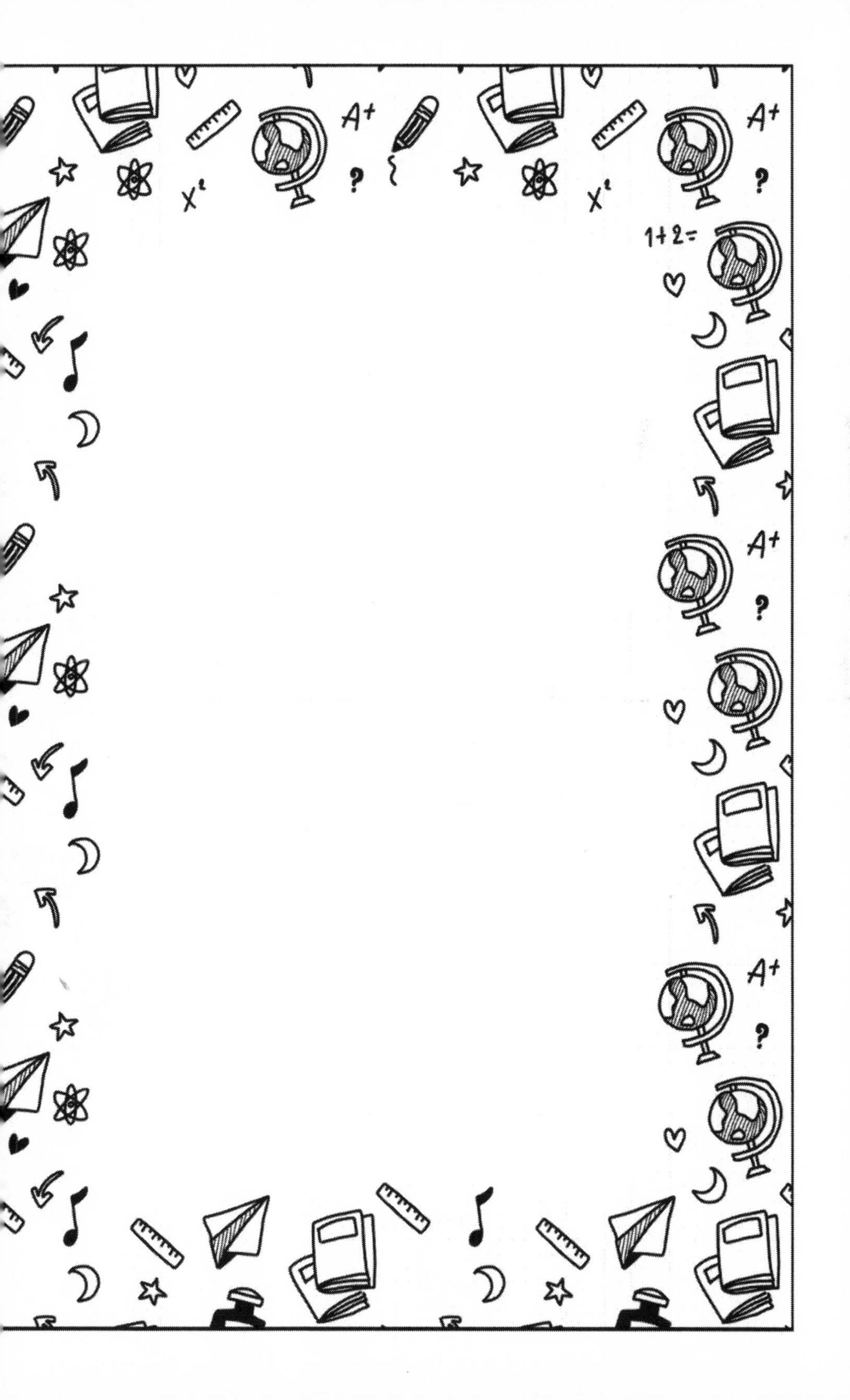

You are
special to me
because

A+
1+2=

A+
?
X²
1+2=
You made
everyone
in class

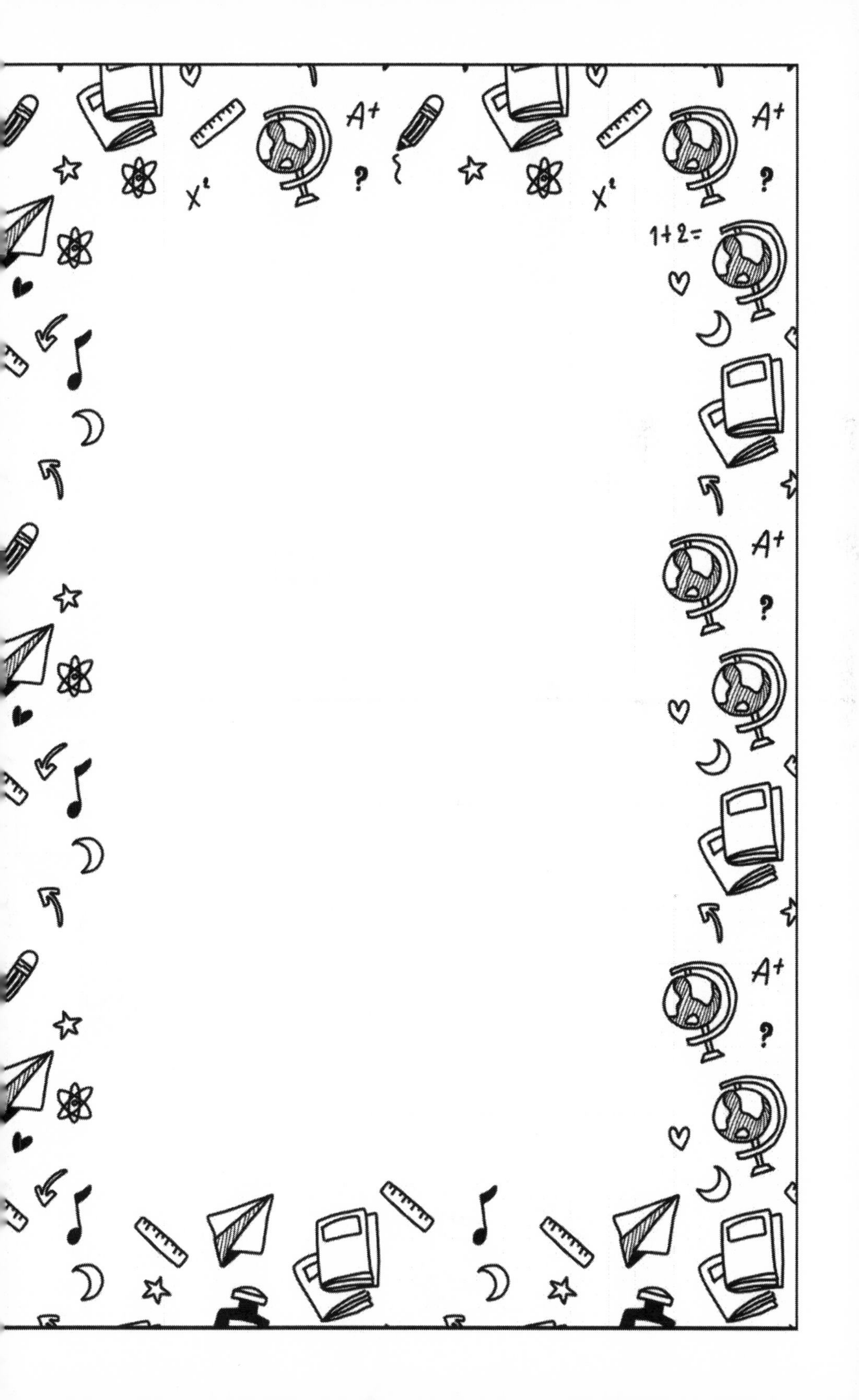

You will
always be my
A+
?
1+2=

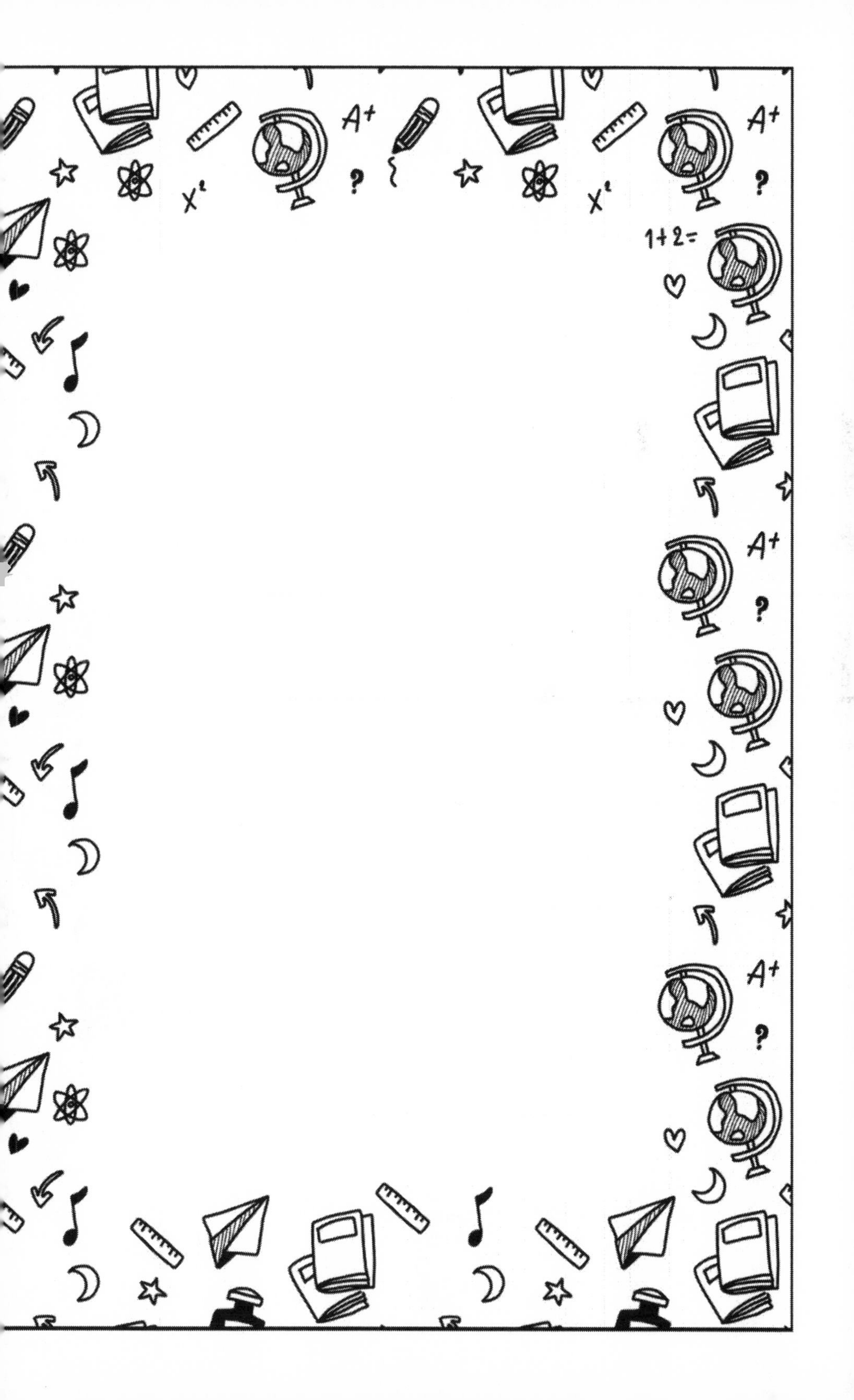

You taught me
how to
A+
?
1+2=

I love when you tell stories about

You inspire
me to do

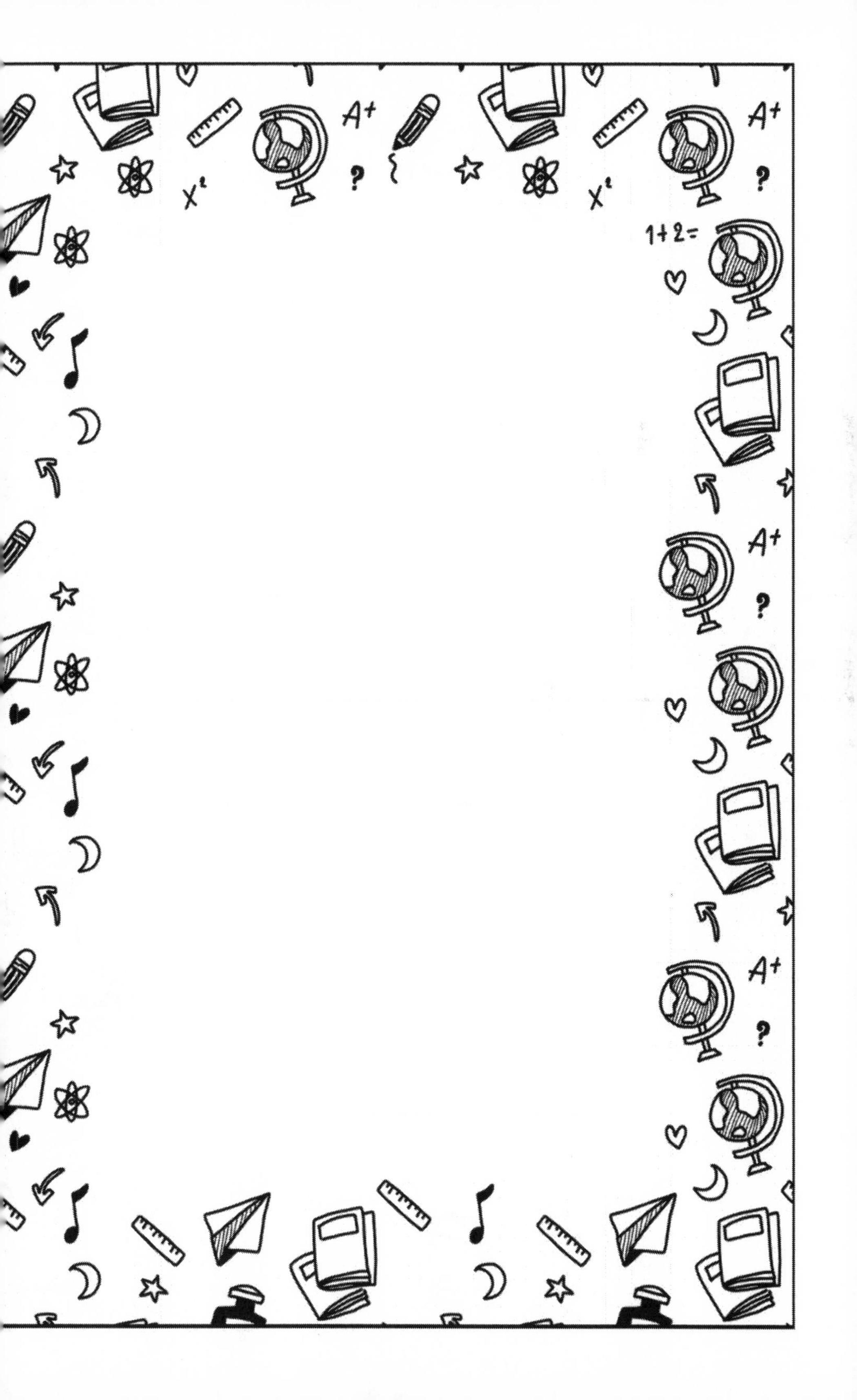

I love you a lot

because

you never

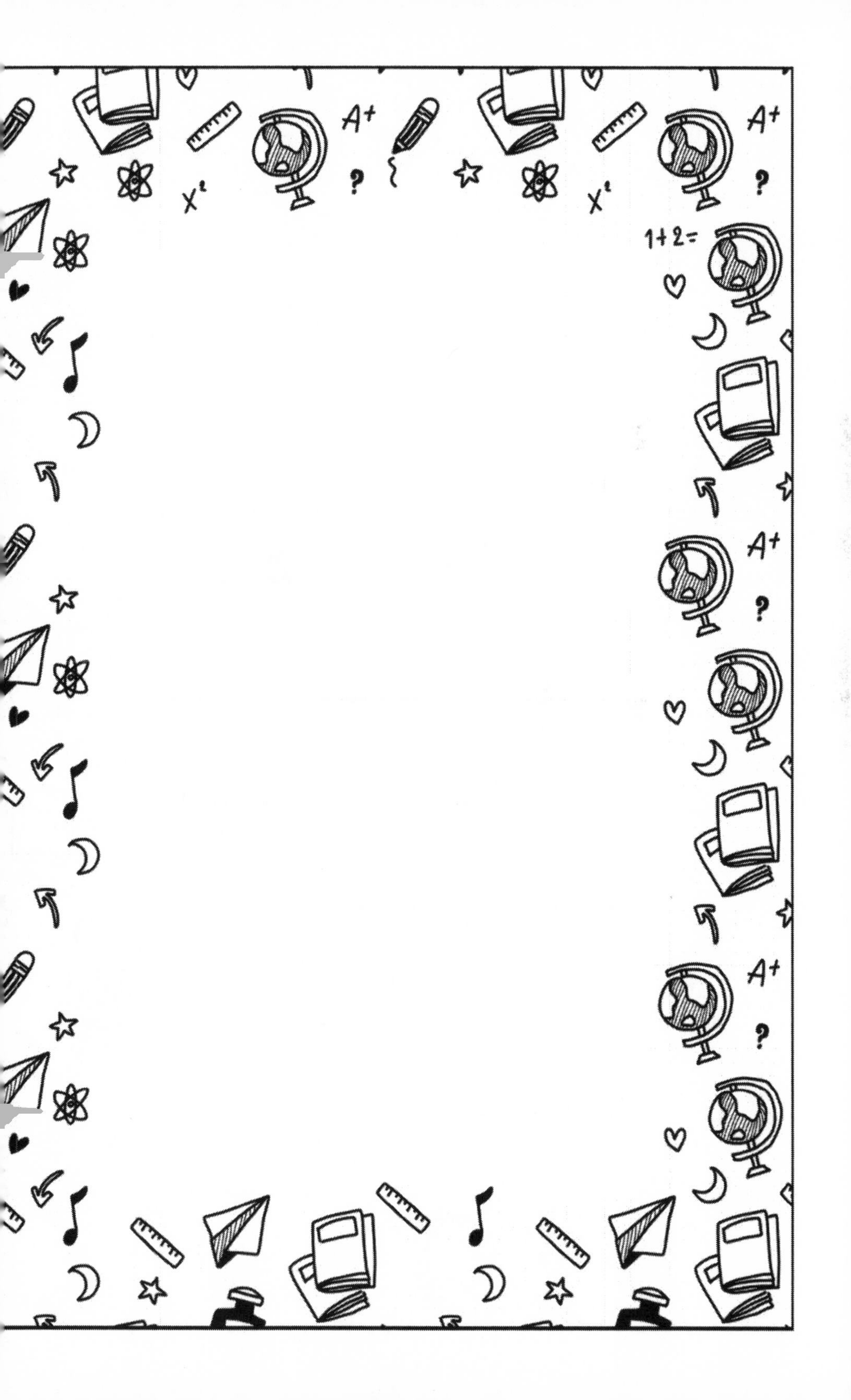
A+
X²
A+
X²
1+2=
A+
A+

Funniest thing you did was

I wish
we had
more time to

I loved when you surprised me with

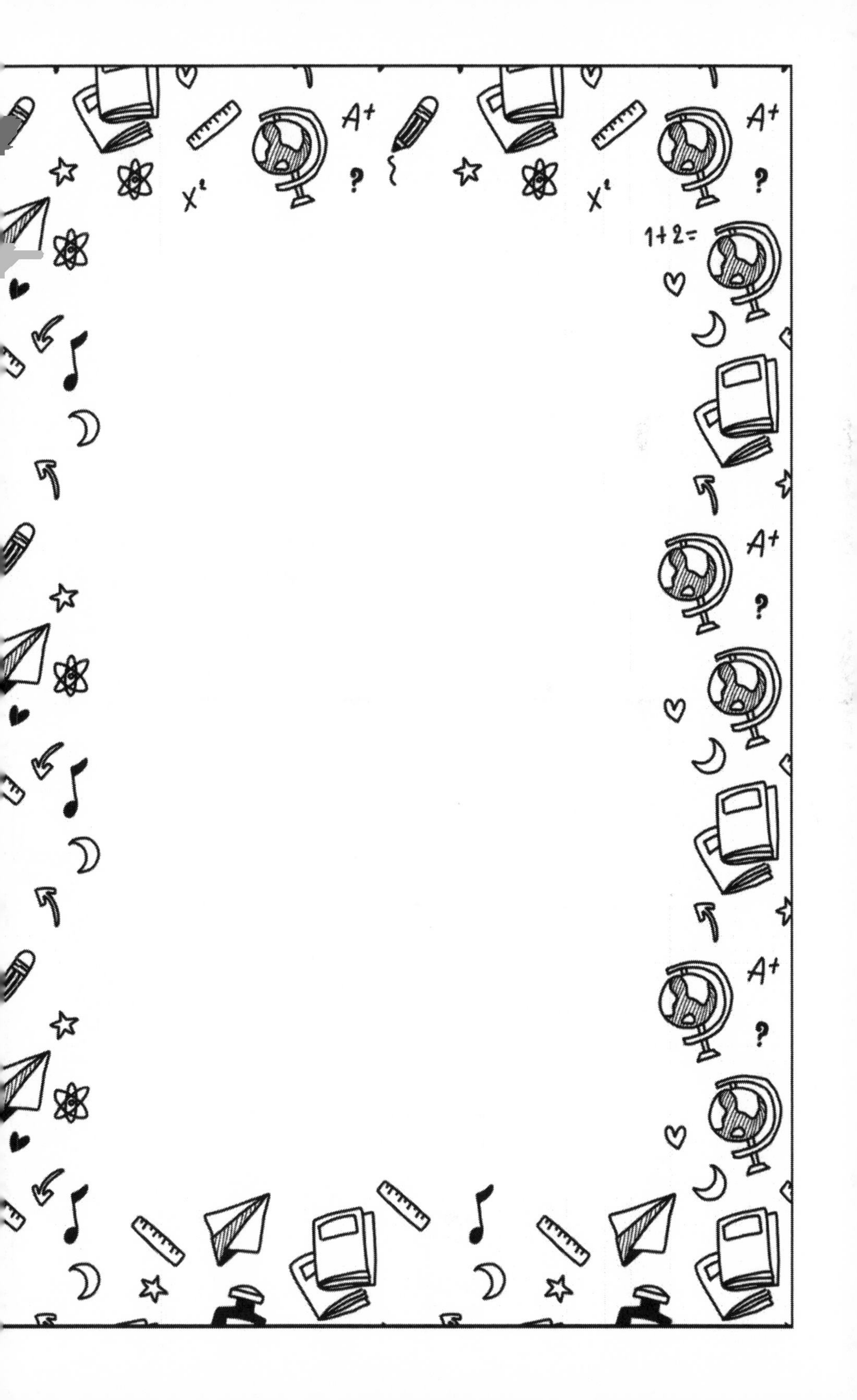
A+
1+2=

I was amazed when you

____

____

____

____

____

____

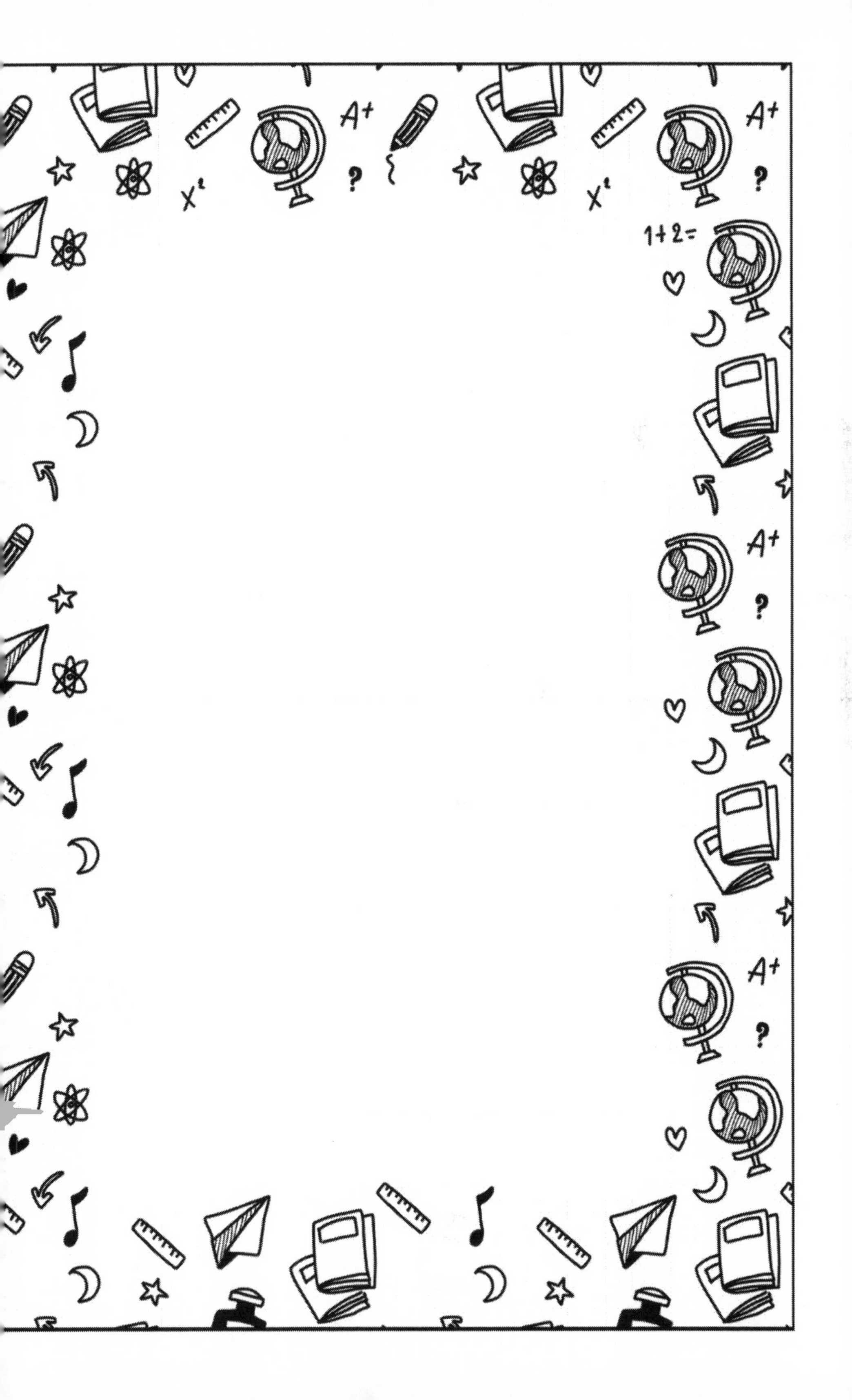
A+
1+2=

You are the kind of person who always

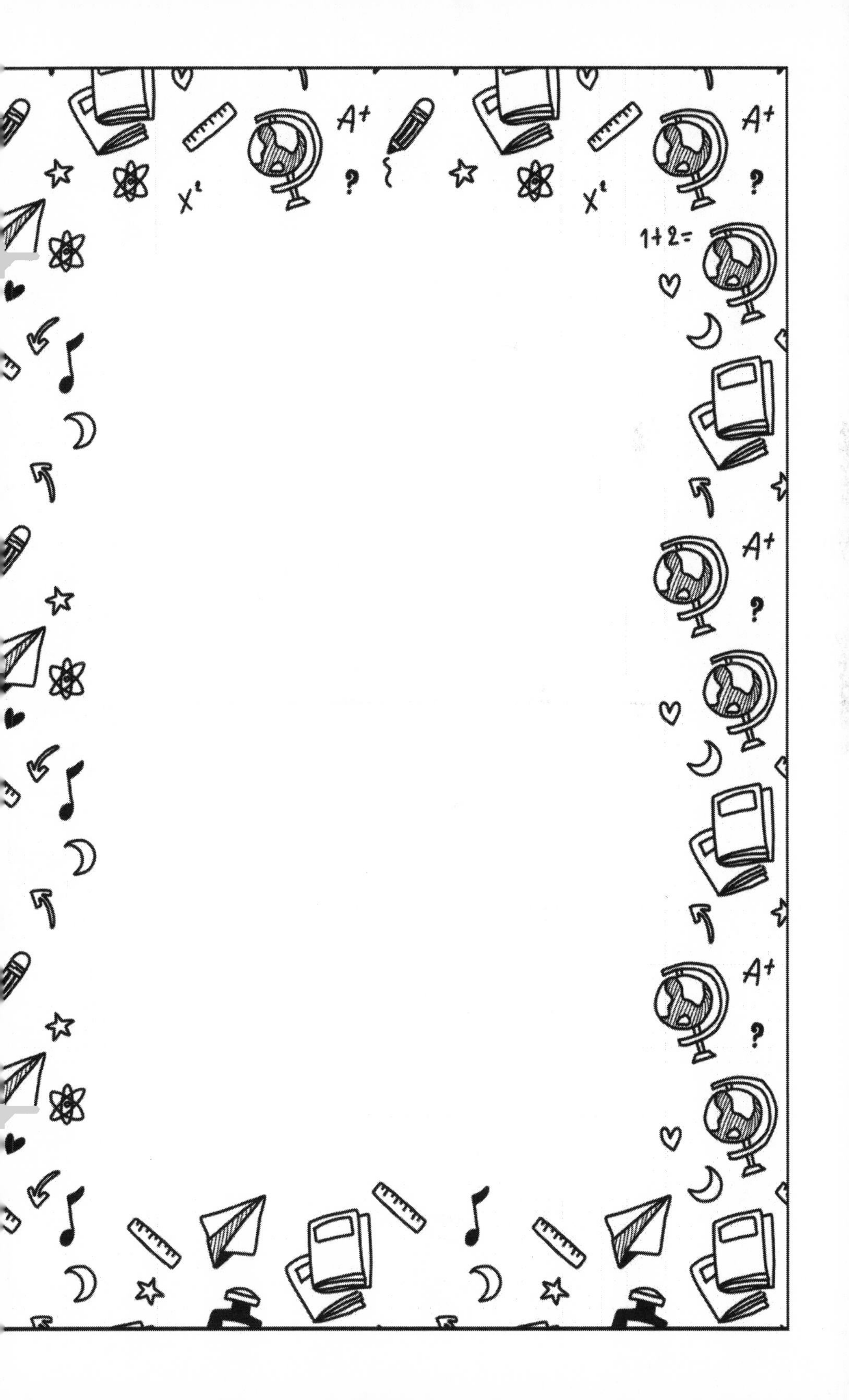

Thank you
for being
A+
A+
A+
A+
1+2=

My favorite thing about you is

I want you

to know that

I will

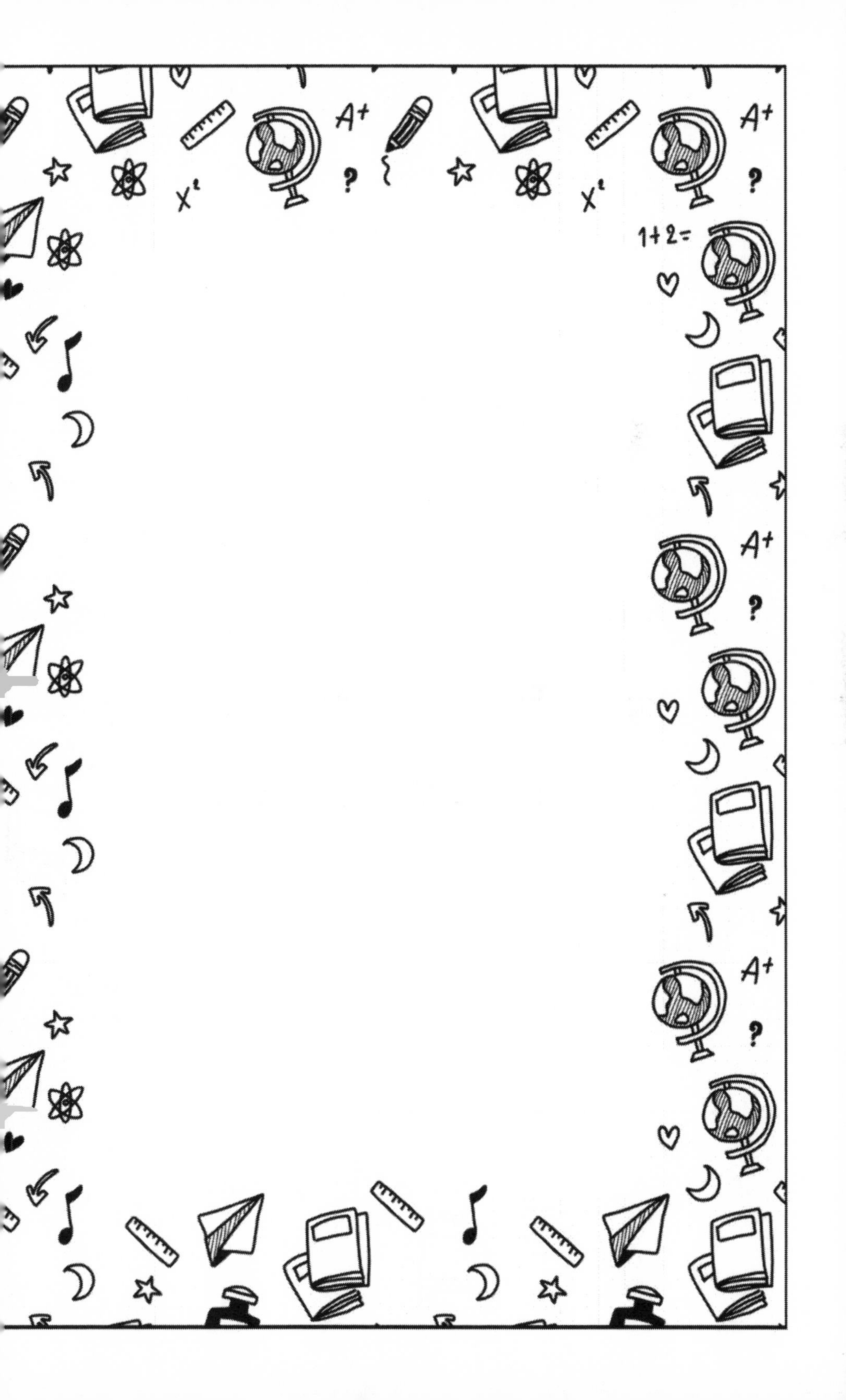

Thank you
for a
wonderful
year!

Made in the USA
Middletown, DE
15 June 2023